WHY THIS IS AN EASY READER

- This story has been carefully written to keep the young reader's interest high.

- It is told in a simple, open style, with a strong rhythm that adds enjoyment both to reading aloud and silent reading.

- There is a very high percentage of words repeated. It is this skillful repetition which helps the child to read independently. Seeing words again and again, he "practices" the vocabulary he knows, and learns with ease the words that are new.

- Only 175 different words have been used, with plurals and root words counted once.

  Well over one-half of the total vocabulary has been used at least three times.

  Over one-fourth of all the words in this story have been used at least six times.

  Some words have been used 15, 20 and 23 times.

ABOUT THIS STORY

- What a happy first way to meet a folk story—and to be able even as an inexperienced reader to get the essential flavor of an old tale! Most youngsters love folk tales, but have to wait to read them until they are more mature readers.

  The play form is a special bonus. It lends itself to tireless re-reading (and learning!), if children are given an opportunity and a little help in acting out the different roles.

The fox who traveled

Story by ALVIN TRESSELT
Pictures by NANCY SEARS
Editorial Consultant: LILIAN MOORE

WONDER BOOKS

A Division of Grosset & Dunlap, Inc.
New York, N. Y. 10010

Introduction

These books are meant to help the young reader discover what a delightful experience reading can be. The stories are such fun that they urge the child to try his new reading skills. They are so easy to read that they will encourage and strengthen him as a reader.

The adult will notice that the sentences aren't too long, the words aren't too hard, and the skillful repetition is like a helping hand. What the child will feel is: "This is a good story—and I can read it myself!"

For some children, the best way to meet these stories may be to hear them read aloud at first. Others, who are better prepared to read on their own, may need a little help in the beginning—help that is best given freely. Youngsters who have more experience in reading alone—whether in first or second or third grade—will have the immediate joy of reading "all by myself."

These books have been planned to help all young readers grow—in their pleasure in books and in their power to read them.

Lilian Moore
Specialist in Reading
Formerly of Division of Instructional Research,
New York City Board of Education

Library of Congress Catalog Card Number: 68-21298

FOX: I have been on my way

all day.

Now I want some supper.

I am very hungry!

(A bee flies by.)

BEE: Buzz, buzz. There is a fox.

I will sting him

on the nose.

FOX: There is a bee.

He is not very big.

But we shall see

what we shall see.

(The bee flies up to sting
the fox.
The fox grabs the bee.
He puts him in his bag.)

9

Now I will go on my way.

Maybe this bee will help

me get a good supper.

10

(He comes to a farmhouse.)

Mr. Farmer, I must go
to town.
Will you look after
my bag until I get back?

11

FARMER: I have been working
all day.
But it is not work
to look after a bag.
I will do it for you.

FOX: One thing, Farmer.
Do not open the bag!
(He runs off
and hides behind a tree.)

FARMER: What can the fox have

in his bag?

I will take one little look.

14

(He opens the bag.
The bee flies out.
A rooster sees the bee
and eats him.)

FOX: Well, Farmer, here I am.

Now I will take my bag.

(He picks up the bag.)

I do not hear

my bee buzzing.

You opened my bag!

Now my bee is gone.

FARMER: I opened it
one little bit.
The bee flew out
and my rooster ate him.

17

FOX: Then you must give me

your rooster.

(He grabs the rooster
and puts him in his bag.)

Good-by, Mr. Farmer.

Next time,

do as you are told.

(He runs off with the rooster
in his bag.)

A rooster will make

a good supper,

but maybe I can do better.

We shall see

what we shall see.

(He comes to an old lady.)

Old Lady,

I must go to town.

Will you look after

my bag until I get back?

OLD LADY: I have been working
all day.
But it is not work
to look after a bag.
Yes, I will do it for you.

22

FOX: One thing, Old Lady.

Do not open the bag!

(He runs off and hides behind a tree.)

OLD LADY: What can the fox

have in his bag?

I will take

one little look.

(She opens the bag.
The rooster flies out,
and her pig runs after him.)

25

FOX: Well, Old Lady,

here I am again.

Now I will take my bag.

(He picks up the bag.)

Old Lady,

I can tell.

You opened my bag.

Now my rooster is gone!

26

OLD LADY: I opened it one little bit.

The rooster flew out.

My pig does not like

roosters.

So he ran

after the rooster.

27

FOX: Then I must have

your pig.

(He grabs the pig and
puts him in his bag.)

Good-by, Old Lady.

Next time,

do as you are told.

(He runs off with the pig
in his bag.)

A rooster is

a good supper.

A pig is a better supper.

But maybe

I can do better.

We shall see

what we shall see.

(He comes to a farmer's
wife.)

Good Lady,

I must go to town.

Will you look after

my bag until I get back?

30

FARMER'S WIFE: I have been working

all day.

But it is no work

to look after a bag.

Yes, I will do it

for you.

31

FOX: One thing, Good Lady.

Do not open the bag!

(He runs off
and hides behind a tree.)

33

FARMER'S WIFE: What can the fox

have in his bag?

It looks so big and fat.

He will not know

if I take one little look.

34

(She opens the bag.
Out jumps the pig.
Her little boy runs after
the pig.
The pig jumps over a wall
and runs away.)

FOX: Ah, Good Lady,

here I am again.

Now I will take

my bag and go.

36

(He sees the bag lying
open on the ground.)

You opened my bag!

Now my pig is gone!

37

FARMER'S
WIFE:
I opened it

one little bit.

The pig jumped out,

and my little boy

ran after it.

Now the pig

has run away.

FOX: Then I must take your little boy.

(He puts the little boy in the
bag and runs away before
the farmer's wife can stop
him.)

Good-by, Good Lady!

Next time,

do as you are told.

(He runs into the woods.)

42

A rooster is a good supper.

A pig is a better supper.

But a little boy

is the best supper!

I will put my bag here.

Now I must make a fire,
but first, I must look
for some wood.

(He goes to look
for some wood.
A man comes by
with his dog.
He is a hunter.
He hears
the little boy crying.)

45

HUNTER: Why is that bag
on the ground?
And why do I hear
a child crying?

(He opens the bag and
the little boy comes out.)

What is this all about?

Why are you in the bag?

LITTLE
BOY:

A fox put me in his bag.

Now he is going to eat me

for his supper.

49

HUNTER: Is that so?

(He puts his dog in the bag.)

Now we shall see

what we shall see.

50

(The hunter and the
little boy hide in the woods.
Soon the fox comes back
with wood for his fire.)

FOX: Now let me see
the fat little boy
I will have for my supper!

52

(He opens the bag
and out jumps the dog.)

This is not my supper!

Help! Help!

(He runs away as fast
as he can go, with the dog
running after him.)

HUNTER: Mr. Fox will not have
any supper tonight!
Now I will take you
home to your mother.

(The fox runs away
from the dog.
He hides in a deep hole.)

FOX: Why was I so greedy?

A boy is better

than a pig.

A pig is better

than a rooster.

58

And a rooster is better

than a bee.

59

Now I do not even have

one little bee

for my supper!

CHOOSE FROM THESE EASY READERS